SPARK ISLAND

English

LEARNING ADVENTURES

For Ages

9-11
English

BBC

SPARK ISLAND
www.sparkisland.com

BBC

English

Ages
9-11

CD-ROM

All Talk
Reel Winner
Rocket Words

Includes parents' notes

Notes for Parents

This book has been created, written and designed by teachers and educationalists to support the development of core English skills linked to the National Curriculum and Scottish Guidelines.

Remember these three key points when you and your child are working:

a) Always pick a quiet time and make sure you have the time to help if your child needs it.

b) Offer help when your child asks for it; don't rush in with advice.

c) Talk about what activities your child likes and why they like those activities.

The Spark Island Gang

Hi! I'm Strat. I will help you through the practice sessions and sometimes give you some hints about Milo's challenges.

Hi! My name is Zeb and, if you believe my parents, I know everything! I hope I will be able to help you through the Maths books and make sure you do well in Milo's challenges. Good luck!

Hi! I'm Dotty and I will help you through the English books with Nina and the rest of the gang. I love English, especially writing stories.

I'm Nina and it's my job to keep this gang on its feet. I'll also keep an eye on Milo, even when he's setting the silliest challenges.

OK, I may be the youngest of the gang but with my baseball cap I set the challenges. Watch out for me on every page. I can help you get extra megahops.

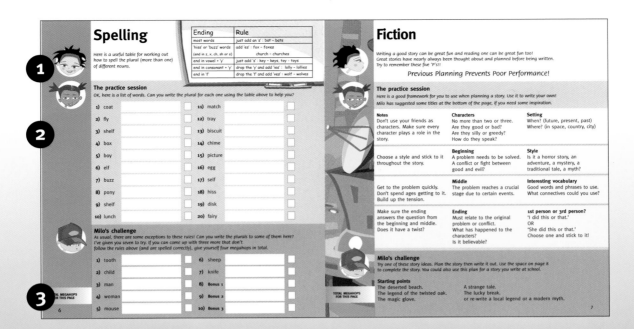

How This Book Works

1 Dotty's section

Dotty gives you the low-down on what we are learning on each page as well as examples of how to complete the exercises. Read this section first.

2 The practice session

Gives you the essential practice in the key concepts and helps you prepare for the Challenge. Each practice question gets you megahops!

3 Milo's challenge

A trickier set of questions designed to test your knowledge and skills. You can win extra megahops in this section but watch out... the questions are tricky!

The game

Use your megahops when you play the game on page 12. The more megahops you have, the better you can do in the game.

CD-ROM support

This feature lets you know that there is a great game to play on the CD-ROM that covers just this topic!

The answers

We have put the answers on page 24. At the end of each page check your answers then tally up your megahops and total your score. Megahops allow you to compete in the Sparkopolis Challenge in the centre pages of the book. Good luck!

Using the CD-ROM and website

The Spark Island CD-ROM that comes with this book provides three activities to do on your computer, as well as a bank of activity sheets that you can print out and complete. We recommend using the CD-ROM after each page with the CD symbol on it, however this is just a guide and using the activities on the computer at any time will help you to practise the important skills.

Our website, www.sparkisland.com, contains a wealth of activities and further useful parents' notes. The website is currently being used in schools across the UK and so you can be confident that it will help your child to succeed.

Nouns and pronouns

Remember what nouns are? That's right, they name things like people, animals, objects and places.

- Common nouns are most nouns, naming types of things.
- Proper nouns are nouns that name people, places or things. They usually have capital letters.
- Collective nouns name groups of things.

The practice session

Can you put these nouns into the correct boxes?

October	Gaggle	Balloon	Pat	Apple	France	Picture
Bunch	Book	Flock	James	Tribe	Candle	Pacific

Common nouns ☐

Proper nouns ☐

Collective nouns ☐

Pronouns take the place of nouns, so you don't have to repeat yourself. Here is a list of pronouns. Can you make them fit the sentences?

Milo took off his baseball cap and put it on the chair.

'It' is used instead of 'baseball cap'.

it	me	he	yours	mine	she

1) Leave that drink alone. It's ☐ ! ☐

2) The first time Zeb saw his computer he thought ☐ looked very cool! ☐

3) Strat was able to tell Dotty that ☐ wanted to learn his tables. ☐

4) "It's time for ☐ to go home," said Milo. ☐

5) Nina thought ☐ would try the next challenge. ☐

6) "The drink is ☐ ," I told him. ☐

Milo's challenge

How many pronouns, collective nouns and common nouns can you spot in this paragraph? Give yourself half a megahop each time you circle one.

☐ ☐
☐ ☐

TOTAL MEGAHOPS FOR THIS PAGE ☐

The football team tried to help Milo, who was struggling with a flock of birds circling his rocket. They shouted at the flock to scare it away. The birds flew off and Milo could launch his rocket.

2

Verbs

The tense of a verb tells you when it is happening.
It can be past, present or future.
Let's look at some examples on the board.

Dotty <u>was playing</u> the best pinball game.
(past)

Dotty <u>plays</u> the best pinball game.
(present)

Dotty <u>will play</u> the best pinball game.
(future)

The practice session

Can you re-write these sentences in the tense I'm asking for?

1) Jim will fix the car. (past)

2) Davy loved playing his guitar. (present)

3) We are waiting for the bus. (past)

4) The paint took ages to dry. (future)

5) Dotty will finish her homework.

(present)

If you write something from your point of view (I did this, I did that) then that is called the **first person**.

If you are talking to your reader (you are, you will), that is called the **second person**.

Writing about someone or something (he did, she will, the chair) is called the **third person**.

Can you circle the correct 'person' that each sentence is written in?

1) I cycled home last night. FIRST SECOND THIRD

2) Martin quickly shook the spider off his arm. FIRST SECOND THIRD

3) Before you pass the ketchup, blow your nose. FIRST SECOND THIRD

4) Nina crossed the road with her pet chicken. FIRST SECOND THIRD

5) I can't remember where I lost the ball. FIRST SECOND THIRD

Milo's challenge

Can you untangle this sentence and re-write it
in the 'past tense' and the 'third person'?

swimming am sea. I in the

Adjectives

Adjectives are describing words. They tell you more about a noun. They make the difference between dull writing and interesting writing. Simple as that!

- Zeb is really <u>clever</u>.
- It was <u>hot</u> so I drank a <u>long</u>, <u>cold</u> drink.
- Dotty is a very <u>funny</u> girl.

The practice session

Can you choose an adjective from the box to liven up each of these sentences?

scary	shiny	blue	wide	shy	new	dirty	warm	gaping	large

1) The rock star was really a _____ person. ☐

2) His hand shook over the _____ button. ☐

3) The striker struck the ball into the _____ net. ☐

4) Zeb and Milo ran across the _____ road. ☐

5) Dotty and Strat played their _____ guitars. ☐

6) David and Jamie opened the _____ box. ☐

7) Julia walked towards the _____ castle. ☐

8) It was a _____ evening when they left the house. ☐

9) The _____ parrot flew into the trees. ☐

10) My _____ shoes needed a good clean. ☐

Milo's challenge

Can you write three new adjectives to describe these four nouns?

(Two extra megahops if you DON'T use colours!)

tree	**soup**	**squirrel**	**lake**	
gnarled	delicious	nervous	deep	
				☐
				☐
				☐

TOTAL MEGAHOPS
FOR THIS PAGE ☐

4

Spelling

There are lots of strategies you can use to improve your spelling. I've written one on the board that can help you to remember tricky words.

Try to make a phrase from the letters of the word you want to remember. This is called a mnemonic.

For example COUGH

Colds **Open** **Up** **Green** **Hankies**

The practice session

Can you write a phrase to help you spell the following words?

1) Known

2) Future

3) Produce

4) Surprise

5) Ready

Another way is to 'personalise' a word so that you always remember how to spell it.
I do this by breaking up words into steps. For example, Wednesday becomes Wed-nes-day.

Business can then become bus-i-ness which helps me to remember the number of 's's.

Try to break these words into manageable steps for you to remember.

1) Designed

2) Technique

3) Injured

4) Attempts

5) Scratched

Milo's challenge

Write down five words of your own that you find difficult to spell (use a dictionary).
Now write a phrase or 'personalise' each one until you can spell them all. Test yourself, and then ask a friend to test you. Give yourself one megahop for each word you get right.

TAL MEGAHOPS OR THIS PAGE

Spelling

Here is a useful table for working out how to spell the plural (more than one) of different nouns.

Ending	Rule
most words	just add an 's': bat – bats
'hiss' or 'buzz' words (end in z, x, ch, sh or s)	add 'es': fox – foxes / church – churches
end in vowel + 'y'	just add 's': key – keys, toy – toys
end in consonant + 'y'	drop the 'y' and add 'ies': lolly – lollies
end in 'f'	drop the 'f' and add 'ves': wolf – wolves

The practice session

OK, here is a list of words. Can you write the plural for each one using the table above to help you?

1) coat

2) fly

3) shelf

4) box

5) boy

6) elf

7) buzz

8) pony

9) wolf

10) lunch

11) match

12) tray

13) biscuit

14) chime

15) picture

16) egg

17) self

18) hiss

19) disk

20) fairy

Milo's challenge

As usual, there are some exceptions to these rules! Can you write the plurals to some of them here? I've given you seven to try.

If you can come up with three more that don't follow the rules above (and are spelled correctly), give yourself three extra megahops.

1) tooth

2) child

3) man

4) woman

5) mouse

6) sheep

7) knife

8) **Bonus 1**

9) **Bonus 2**

10) **Bonus 3**

TOTAL MEGAHOPS FOR THIS PAGE

Fiction

Writing a good story can be great fun and reading one can be great fun too!

Great stories have nearly always been thought about and planned before being written. Try to remember these five 'P's!!

Previous Planning Prevents Poor Performance!

The practice session

Here is a good framework for you to use when planning a story. Use it to write your own!

Milo has suggested some titles at the bottom of the page, if you need some inspiration.

Notes
Don't use your friends as characters. Make sure every character plays a role in the story.

Characters
No more than two or three.
Are they good or bad?
Are they silly or greedy?
How do they speak?

Setting
When? (future, present, past)
Where? (in space, country, city)

Choose a style and stick to it throughout the story.

Beginning
A problem needs to be solved.
A conflict or fight between good and evil?

Style
Is it a horror story, an adventure, a mystery, a traditional tale, a myth?

Get to the problem quickly. Don't spend ages getting to it. Build up the tension.

Middle
The problem reaches a crucial stage due to certain events.

Interesting vocabulary
Good words and phrases to use. What connectives could you use?

Make sure the ending answers the question from the beginning and middle. Does it have a twist?

Ending
Must relate to the original problem or conflict.
What has happened to the characters?
Is it believable?

1st person or 3rd person?
'I did this or that.'
OR
'She did this or that.'
Choose one and stick to it!

Milo's challenge

Try one of these story ideas. Plan the story then write it out. Use the space on page 8 to complete the story. You could also use this plan for a story you write at school.

Starting points
The deserted beach.
A strange tale.
The legend of the twisted oak.
The lucky break.
The magic glove.
Or re-write a local legend or a modern myth.

Fiction

Here is a chance for you to write a short story. Choose a title from page 7, plan the story using the format on the same page and have a go.

Try to keep to the sections below. If you need more space, you can use your own paper.

Grab the reader's attention!

Title

Beginning

Check your p

Build up the tension!

Middle

Check your p

Tie up all the loose ends!

Ending

Check your p

Milo's challenge

Make sure you edit your work. Check the following:

a) Re-read your story – does it make sense?

b) Check your punctuation – capitals, full stops, speech marks and so on.

c) Spelling and grammar – put what you know into practice.

d) Paragraphing – does each new paragraph introduce a new idea, change of character speaking or location?

Prepositions

Prepositions are often used to tell the reader _where_ things are and _when_ they happen. Look at the board.

Milo ducked <u>under</u> the bar.

Dotty was tired <u>after</u> she had run the marathon.

The practice session

Have a go at these. Can you add a suitable preposition to these sentences?

into	until	before	after	behind	through	off	across	over	at

1) Simon knew he had got himself _____ trouble. ☐

2) The shark circled twice _____ moving in for the kill. ☐

3) The fan held his breath as the striker shouted _____ the ref. ☐

4) Peter looked _____ Jane and saw the huge monster's eyes. ☐

5) Janet climbed _____ the hole into the forest. ☐

6) John threw the ball _____ the fence and smashed the window. ☐

7) Tim saw his sister _____ the road. ☐

8) Bill went home as soon as he was sent _____ . ☐

9) It was not until _____ the show that Dotty realised her mistake. ☐

10) 'Don't leave _____ I've told you to go!' shouted Mr Cooper. ☐

Milo's challenge

Can you put the correct preposition in the space to make these phrases make sense?

agree _____	Zeb	into	☐
inspired _____	his idea	on	☐
rely _____	Milo	of	☐
guilty _____	a crime	over	☐
plunge _____	the river	with	☐
lean _____	the wall	by	☐

Sentences – subordinate clauses

Complex sentences have main clauses and subordinate clauses. But what does this mean? The main clause makes sense on its own but the subordinate clause doesn't.
Let's take a closer look!

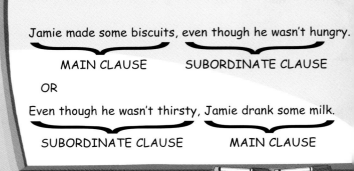

Jamie made some biscuits, even though he wasn't hungry.

MAIN CLAUSE   SUBORDINATE CLAUSE

OR

Even though he wasn't thirsty, Jamie drank some milk.

SUBORDINATE CLAUSE   MAIN CLAUSE

The practice session

Can you match the subordinate clause with a main clause? See which one fits the best!

1) I escaped from the ship · · · yet I still woke up with a sore head. ☐

2) The newspaper flapped wildly · · · in fact that's all he does all day. ☐

3) The pillow was very comfy, · · · even though I can't sing a note. ☐

4) My cat loves sleeping, · · · just before it blew up. ☐

5) I would love to be a pop star, · · · due to the heavy gust of wind. ☐

6) My calculator didn't work · · · so she could catch her train. ☐

7) Zeb ate a huge lunch · · · as well as the door. ☐

8) Dotty had to leave early · · · before the skate competition. ☐

9) The window was open · · · before the cup final. ☐

10) We had a warm up · · · because the batteries had run out. ☐

Milo's challenge

I've got three subordinate clauses (lucky me!).
Can you write three main clauses in front of them so they make sense?

1) [   ] , despite having one leg! ☐

2) [   ] , whilst angrily jumping up and down. ☐

3) [   ] , before tumbling down the stairs. ☐

Sentences – connectives

Now you know a bit more about complex sentences, let's look at <u>connectives</u>. These are the words and phrases that connect different parts of a text.

- Milo got a new baseball cap for his birthday <u>and</u> loved it.

- The movie was great <u>because</u> it was so funny.

The practice session

Add a suitable connective to each of these sentences and then finish each one.

**because   and   in other words   but   meanwhile   therefore   also
however   on the other hand   finally   nevertheless   after all**

1) The chair was rather elegant **because** of its hand-carved legs. ✔

2) Most children play happily

3) The flowers drooped sadly

4) I love going to the cinema

5) Ice creams are popular in the summer

6) It was a long time to travel

7) We can't start the game yet

8) Dotty has arrived

9) The shed looked rather weather beaten

10) The bird swooped low

Milo's challenge

OK, have you understood connectives yet? If so, you won't have any trouble writing four sentences using different connectives.

1)

2)

3)

4)

Chart Idol

Make sure you've done all the exercises in the book before playing the game.

Enter your total megahops here:

What is your pop rating?

250+ megahops	**200–249** megahops	**150–199** megahops	**100–149** megahops	**Less than 100** megahops
Pop God! You are a household name and are asked to perform at royal events.	A-List Celebrity! Everyone wants to know you and you play live on Top of the Pops.	Wannabe. You are on the edge of greatness. Just one more bit of luck and you will make it!	One-hit wonder. It was great while it lasted but that was only for a couple of weeks!	Has-been. You can only get work on game shows and you find your CDs in the bargain buckets!

How to play

1) Work out what pop rating you have using the chart above.

2) Now use a dice to move up the chart from 50 to Number 1.

3) You can gain and lose megahops on the way round.

4) If you lose all your megahops you lose the game.

5) The winner is the first person to get a Number 1 with the highest possible pop rating.

6) Good luck!

1 Chart Idol

2 Appear in latest edition of Teen Magazine
Win 30 megahops

3

4 Asked to appear on daytime TV
Win 20 megahops

5

6 Spotted out shopping with your mum
Lose 30 megahops

7

8

9

10 Your single is not on the radio playlist
Lose 30 megahops

11

12

13 Have to go back to school to finish your exams
Lose 20 megahops

14

15 Appear in latest edition of Teen Magazine
Win 30 megahops

16

17 Your single is not on the radio playlist
Lose 30 megahops

18 Your CD is reviewed by the music press – they love it
Win 50 megahops

19

20 Get spotted by a top manager
Win 30 megahops

21

22 Appear in latest edition of Teen Magazine
Win 30 megahops

23

24 Your CD is reviewed by the music press – they love it
Win 50 megahops

25 Your single is not on the radio playlist
Lose 30 megahops

26

27 Photographed being mean to your little sister
Lose 50 megahops

28 Appear in latest edition of Teen Magazine
Win 30 megahops

29

30 Asked to appear on daytime TV
Win 20 megahops

31

32 Appear in latest edition of Teen Magazine
Win 30 megahops

33 Spotted out shopping with your mum
Lose 30 megahops

34 Asked to appear on daytime TV
Win 20 megahops

35

36 Your single is not on the radio playlist
Lose 30 megahops

37 Have to go back to school to finish your exams
Lose 20 megahops

38 Oversleep and miss the first date of your tour
Lose 80 megahops

39

40 Your CD is reviewed by the music press – they love it
Win 50 megahops

41

42 Get spotted by a top manager
Win 30 megahops

43

44 Photographed being mean to your little sister
Lose 50 megahops

45

46 Your single is not on the radio playlist
Lose 30 megahops

47

48 Madonna wants to do a duet with you
Win 80 megahops

49

50

Punctuation

Remember the easy stuff?
Full stops mark the end of a sentence.
Question marks show the end of a question.
Exclamation marks indicate the end of a strong emotional sentence.

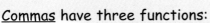

<u>Commas</u> have three functions:
- They are used to separate items in a list.
- They are used to separate pieces of information in a sentence – a bit like brackets.
- They are used to separate clauses.

The practice session

Can you punctuate these sentences?

1) The children munched their burgers happily ☐

2) Stop eating, this minute ☐

3) Lunch time was over ☐

4) What's our next lesson ☐

5) I HATE Geography ☐

6) Is it nearly home time yet ☐

Do you remember all about commas?
Commas are meant to help the reader make sense of a sentence.
Can you put commas into these sentences to give them their true meaning?

1) The woman was run over while jogging in an awful way. ☐

2) The father bought a toy for the baby with purple hair. ☐

3) The shoes which are my favourites are black. ☐

4) The shed collapsed in the wind making a big bang. ☐

Milo's challenge

OK, your turn now. Can you write three sentences like the ones above, which have different meanings when the commas are removed?

1) Without commas ☐

   With commas ☐

2) Without commas ☐

   With commas ☐

3) Without commas ☐

   With commas ☐

Punctuation

Let's try some new punctuation, which will make your writing even more radical! Let's look at colons!

A colon is placed just before a list begins. For example:
The Spark gang took the following items on holiday:
5 towels, 5 swimming costumes, 5 surfboards and Milo's teddy.

Hey, I thought you weren't going to tell anyone about that!

The practice session

Don't worry Milo. Can you put the colons in these sentences?

1) I play the following sports football, cricket and bowls. ☐

2) My CD collection contains ACDC, ABC, U2 and UB40. ☐

3) For lunch we will be serving soup, chicken pie and chips, ice cream and coffee. ☐

4) The Spark Gang is made up of Dotty, Strat, Milo, Zeb and Nina. ☐

5) I study these subjects Literacy, Numeracy, Science, Geography and History. ☐

Now we are going to look at semi-colons (;).

Can you put a semi-colon in each of the following sentences?

Two equally important but separate sentences can be joined together by a semi-colon.

1) Start the engine check your fuel tank. ☐

2) Grill the fish pour over the sauce. ☐

3) Remember to wash your face clean your teeth before bed. ☐

4) Steer the boat towards the dock watch out for the rocks. ☐

5) Nearly time for supper beans on toast tonight. ☐

Milo's challenge

Semi-colons can also be used to break up long lists and phrases.
I've taken out five semi-colons. Can you put them in the right places?

At the skatepark there were skaters on the half-pipe skaters in the bowl a freestyle competition some top tunes on the sound system a stall selling clothes and the cool boarder Milo.

TAL MEGAHOPS OR THIS PAGE ☐

15

Punctuation

You should know how to use speech marks by now. Remember, they show the words that someone has actually spoken.

"Put the torch on," Dave whispered.
"Shine it at the monster."
(direct speech)

Reported speech does not need speech ma[rks]

Dave told me to put the torch on and shine it at the monster.
(reported speech)

The practice session

Using the word 'said' can get a little bit boring in speech.
Here are some other words that you can use instead.

shouted	growled	whispered	cried	laughed	called

Can you write six sentences in direct speech?
Use the words above to make your sentences more interesting.
Here's an example.

> "Hey! Get off that fence," yelled the farmer.

1) ☐

2) ☐

3) ☐

4) ☐

5) ☐

6) ☐

Milo's challenge

This is a reported conversation. Can you use speech marks and write out the actual words spoken? You get four megahops for getting all the marks in the right place. Make sure you start a new line for a new speaker.

Zeb asked Nina why all elephants seemed to have grey trunks. Nina replied that she thought it was because they were all in the same swimming club.

Punctuation

See if you can punctuate the story using:

full stops   exclamation marks   question marks
commas   speech marks   colons

Now we're going to see whether you've had your eyes on the prize!
Here is a short story without any punctuation.
A ☐ will show you that something is missing.

One evening in the steamy jungle ☐ two hyenas ☐ Harry and Henry ☐ were walking home after a day in the hot sun ☐ They had just got to a particularly dark part of the jungle when Harry stopped ☐

☐ You're not still moaning about the heat are you ☐ whispered Harry ☐

☐ No ☐ I thought I heard a noise in the bushes ☐ trembled Henry ☐

Just then ☐ a fierce lion leapt from the bush and gave the two hyenas a real hiding ☐ When the lion had finished ☐ he ran back into the jungle feeling very pleased with himself ☐ Henry and Harry walked home and nursed their wounds ☐ Sadly ☐ the following week the same thing happened again ☐ Henry and Harry received another beating ☐

Anyway ☐ a couple of weeks later ☐ Harry and Henry were walking back home as usual ☐

☐ If that pesky lion is waiting for us tonight ☐ let's both team up and fight him off ☐ said Harry bravely ☐

☐ Good idea ☐ replied Henry ☐ as they both approached the dark part of the jungle ☐ Sure enough ☐ the lion leapt out ☐

☐ Rooooaaaarr ☐ roared the lion as the fight started ☐ However ☐ when the fight was over ☐ Harry was cowering up the nearest tree and Henry was sprawled on the floor ☐ battered and bruised ☐

☐ Why didn't you help me ☐ groaned Henry ☐

Harry crawled down ☐ Sorry ☐ You were laughing so much ☐ I thought you were winning ☐ ☐

How did you do? Give yourself a megahop score out of 10.

☐☐☐☐☐☐☐☐☐☐   17

Synonyms

Synonyms are words that have the same (or very similar meaning) to one another. They can add variety to your writing when you use them correctly.

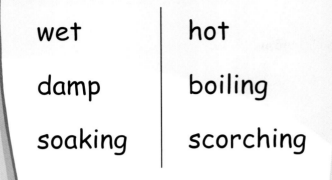

wet	hot
damp	boiling
soaking	scorching

The practice session

OK, we are going to try to find the synonyms for the words below.
Circle all the synonyms in the list.
Remember there may be more than one!

1) **small**	tiny	strong	sleepy	little	☐
2) **big**	great	sad	awful	huge	☐
3) **difficult**	upset	hard	easy	wall	☐
4) **cold**	freezing	boiling	chilly	young	☐
5) **hot**	good	slow	boiling	warm	☐
6) **purchase**	colossal	dainty	acquire	buy	☐
7) **famous**	people	celebrated	well-known	sincere	☐
8) **brave**	under	heroic	fearful	bold	☐
9) **afraid**	fearful	coat	related	sincere	☐
10) **help**	support	light	found	angry	☐

Milo's challenge

Let's see how many synonyms you can find for these two words.
Write them in a list. Use a Thesaurus to check your answers. You should be able to find one in the library.

Small ☐

Big ☐

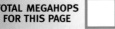

TOTAL MEGAHOPS FOR THIS PAGE ☐

Antonyms

Antonyms are words with meanings that are opposite to one another.

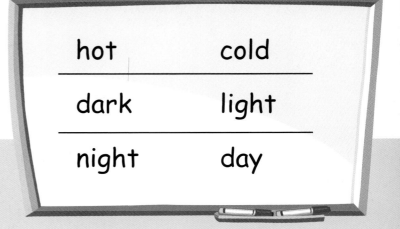

hot	cold
dark	light
night	day

The practice session

OK, we are going to try to find
the antonyms for the words below.
Circle the antonym in the list.
Can you think of any more antonyms?
Write them in the space provided.

1)	**tall**	bring	short	rough	smooth		☐
2)	**wide**	narrow	helpful	daring	appeal		☐
3)	**below**	clean	first	above	new		☐
4)	**dirty**	soft	feeble	require	clean		☐
5)	**under**	awake	stone	over	need		☐
6)	**awake**	funnel	smile	asleep	ready		☐
7)	**foolish**	wheeze	wise	witty	awake		☐
8)	**true**	great	unwise	false	hopeful		☐
9)	**heavy**	exit	oval	light	release		☐
10)	**run**	hop	sprint	walk	swim		☐
11)	**cruel**	face	kind	happy	king		☐
12)	**rough**	smooth	friend	old	bark		☐

Milo's challenge

That shouldn't have been too hard as the
answers were given for you. Try these four
and come up with an antonym using just
your brain! You can check your answers using
a Thesaurus. Your computer might have one too!
The first two are pretty easy though!

1) comfortable ☐
2) straight ☐
3) necessary ☐
4) friend ☐

TAL MEGAHOPS
OR THIS PAGE ☐

19

Sparkopolis

Chapter 1

Strat, Zeb, Nina, Dotty and Milo had escaped from Grunge Hall, an orphanage run by the scary Dame Drusilla. They had rowed out to sea in an abandoned rowing boat. After several days at sea, Zeb sighted land on the horizon.

"What do you think that is?" Zeb shouted.

"It looks like an island," said Dotty, who had the best eyesight.

The weird skyline of Sparkopolis loomed into view as the children rowed towards it. At last, they landed on a beach, near an old man with a long white beard. He was standing in the sea and talking to a dolphin! They were pretty sure he was nuts. He introduced himself as the Wizard Gwanwyn. (Now they knew he was nuts!) Some of the children were suspicious of him, as he wore a silver ring just like Drusilla – but finally they accepted his help and agreed to go with him.

The children were amazed by the weird and wonderful buildings of Sparkopolis and the strange creatures that inhabited them: Rumtums, Spironauts, Xyboks and Crombies. They spotted a pair of Malvos, hidden in a dark doorway. These creatures spoke in a strange language and looked at the children's bags longingly. Gwanwyn told the children never to trust a Malvo. The Malvos watched their arrival with interest, and then scurried off to report the news.

A large building appeared on the children's left, with a sign saying 'Sparkanon'. When he saw the huge building, Milo asked what it was and what happened there, but Gwanwyn didn't answer and changed the subject quickly.

As a leader of Sparkopolis, Gwanwyn called a meeting of the Grand Council of Wizards. They were all rather excited by the new arrivals, as they had no children of their own. One of the Council members urged caution:

"Do we really know who they are? Remember the mistake we made with the Malvos!"

Another agreed, "We don't know where they have come from or why they are here?"

After much discussion, the Council decided to let them sleep in one of the many libraries. This was Milo's idea of heaven and, whilst exploring the books, he came across The Wizard Pocket Guide To Spark Island. It was full of interesting information about the island and its inhabitants.

The children were allowed to roam Sparkopolis, but were warned to stay clear of the Malvos and the Yaboos. (Milo looked up both of these in the pocket guide.) Just as they were beginning to feel at home, a boat arrived in Sparkopolis harbour, bringing news of the outside world. Among the newspapers delivered to the Wizards was a two-week-old copy of the Draconian Daily News. The Wizards were horrified to see the headline, 'Wanted! The Grunge Hall Gang', above photos of the children.

Sparkopolis

These questions are about Chapter 1 of Sparkopolis.

1) Circle the phrase that best completes each sentence.

  a) The Gang have escaped from ☐
  i. Spark Island.
  ii. a tall castle on a mountain.
  iii. an orphanage called Grunge Hall.
  iv. a library in Sparkopolis.

  b) The gang are suspicious of Gwanwyn because ☐
  i. he has a ring that reminds them of Drusilla.
  ii. he walks ahead of them towards the city.
  iii. he arranges a Council meeting.
  iv. he has lots of hair.

2) Can you find four words in the story that describe Gwanwyn?

☐ ☐ ☐ ☐

3) What reasons did the Council members give for the gang NOT being allowed to stay on the island?

☐ ☐

4) Put these events from this first chapter in order from 1 to 4. We have done the first one for you. ☐

1 The children escaped from Grunge Hall.

☐ A boat docked on Spark Island.

☐ The Grand Council of Wizards held a meeting.

☐ The children met Gwanwyn.

5) What sort of person do you think Milo is?

What pieces of the text tell you this?

6) Do you think the Malvos are good or bad characters?

What sentences in the story tell you this?

7) Did you enjoy this chapter?

Explain why you did or didn't like it.

Milo's challenge

Well guys, that's how we got to Sparkopolis.
For two extra megahops, can you write a second chapter of the story?
Some of these questions might help:

What were the gang wanted for?   Did the gang see Dame Drusilla again?

What were the Malvos up to?   Did the gang get to stay in Sparkopolis?

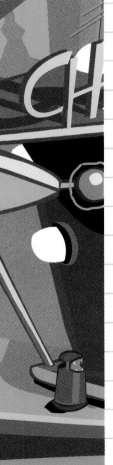

Answers

Page 2
Practice session:
Common nouns –
Book, Balloon, Apple, Candle, Picture
Proper nouns –
October, James, Pat, France, Pacific
Collective nouns –
Bunch, Gaggle, Flock, Tribe
1) mine 2) it 3) he 4) me 5) she
6) yours
Milo's challenge:
Pronouns – his, they, it; Collective
nouns – team, flock;
Common nouns – birds, rocket

Page 3
Practice session:
1) Jim fixed the car. 2) Davy will love
playing his guitar. 3) We were waiting
for the bus. 4) The paint will take ages
to dry. 5) Dotty finishes her homework.

1) First 2) Third 3) Second 4) Third
5) First
Milo's challenge:
Milo swam in the sea.

Page 4
Practice session:
1) shy 2) shiny 3) gaping 4) wide
5) new 6) large 7) scary 8) warm
9) blue 10) dirty
Milo's challenge:
Answers will vary but adjectives should
be appropriate to their subject.

Page 5
Practice session:
1) to 5) Answers will vary.
1) to 5) Answers will vary but could
work like this:
De-sign-ed; Tech-ni-que; In-jured;
At-tempt; Scrat-ched
Milo's challenge:
Answers will vary.

Page 6
Practice session:
1) coats 2) flies 3) shelves 4) boxes
5) boys 6) elves 7) buzzes 8) ponies
9) wolves 10) lunches 11) matches
12) trays 13) biscuits 14) chimes
15) pictures 16) eggs 17) selves 18)
hisses 19) disks 20) fairies
Milo's challenge:
1) teeth 2) children 3) men 4) women
5) mice 6) sheep 7) knives
8) to 10) Answers will vary but should
not obey common conventions.

Pages 7 and 8
Answers will vary.

Page 9
Practice session:
1) into 2) before 3) at 4) behind
5) through 6) over 7) across 8) off
9) after 10) until
Milo's challenge:
agree with; inspired by; rely on; guilty
of; plunge into; lean over

Page 10
Practice session:
1) I escaped from the ship just before
it blew up.
2) The newspaper flapped wildly, due
to the heavy gust of wind.
3) The pillow was very comfy, yet I still
woke up with a sore head.
4) My cat loves sleeping, in fact that's
all he does all day.
5) I would love to be a pop star, even
thought I can't sing a note.
6) My calculator didn't work because
the batteries had run out.
7) Zeb ate a huge lunch before the
skate competition.
8) Dotty had to leave early so she
could catch her train.
9) The window was open as well as
the door.
10) We had a warm up before the cup
final.
Milo's challenge:
Answers will vary.

Page 11
Practice session:
Answers will vary.
Milo's challenge:
Answers will vary.

Page 14
Practice session:
1) . 2) ! 3) . 4) ? 5) ! 6) ?

1) The woman was run over, while
jogging, in an awful way.
2) The father bought a toy for the
baby, with purple hair.
3) The shoes, which are my favourites,
are black.
4) The shed collapsed in the wind,
making a big bang.
Milo's challenge:
Answers will vary.

Page 15
Practice session:
1) I play the following sports: football,
cricket and bowls.
2) My CD collection contains: ACDC,
ABC, U2 and UB40.
3) For lunch we will be serving: soup,
chicken pie and chips, ice cream and
coffee.
4) The Spark Gang is made up of:

Dotty, Strat, Milo, Zeb and Nina.
5) I study these subjects: Literacy,
Numeracy, Science, Geography and
History.

1) Start the engine; check your fuel
tank.
2) Grill the fish; pour over the sauce.
3) Remember to wash your face; clean
your teeth before bed.
4) Steer the boat towards the dock;
watch out for the rocks.
5) Nearly time for supper; beans on
toast tonight.
Milo's challenge:
At the skatepark there were skaters on
the half-pipe; skaters in the bowl; a
freestyle competition; some top tunes
on the sound system; a stall selling
clothes; and the cool boarder Milo.

Page 16
Practice session:
Answers will vary but check that
speech marks are in the right place.
Milo's challenge:
Answers may vary but should be like
this model:
"Nina, why do all the elephants seem
to have grey trunks?" said Milo.
"I thought it was because they were
all in the same swimming club,"
replied Nina.

Page 17
One evening in the steamy jungle, two
hyenas, Harry and Henry, were walking
home after a day in the hot sun. They
had just got to a particularly dark part
of the jungle when Harry stopped.

"You're not still moaning about the
heat are you?" whispered Harry.

"No, I thought I heard a noise in the
bushes," trembled Henry.

Just then, a fierce lion leapt from the
bush and gave the two hyenas a real
hiding. When the lion had finished, he
ran back into the jungle feeling very
pleased with himself. Henry and Harry
walked home and nursed their wounds.

Sadly, the following week the same
thing happened again: Henry and Harry
received another beating!

Anyway, a couple of weeks later, Harry
and Henry were walking home as usual.

"If that pesky lion is waiting for us
tonight, let's both team up and fight
him off," said Harry bravely.

"Good idea!" replied Henry, as they
both approached the dark part of the
jungle. Sure enough, the lion leapt out.

"Rooooaaaarr!" roared the lion as the
fight started. However, when the fight
was over, Harry was cowering up the
nearest tree and Henry was sprawled
on the floor, battered and bruised.

"Why didn't you help me?" groaned
Henry.

Harry crawled down. "Sorry. You were
laughing so much, I thought you were
winning!"

Page 18
Practice session:
1) tiny, little 2) great, huge 3) hard 4)
freezing, chilly 5) boiling, warm 6)
acquire, buy 7) celebrated, well-known
8) heroic, bold 9) fearful 10) support
Milo's challenge:
Answers will vary but could include
some of the following:
Small – minuscule, slight, petite,
unimportant
Big – colossal, gigantic, great, massive,
vast

Page 19
Practice session:
1) short 2) narrow 3) above 4) clean 5)
over 6) asleep 7) wise 8) false 9) light
10) walk 11) kind 12) smooth
Milo's challenge:
Answers will vary but could include:
1) uncomfortable 2) bent
3) unnecessary 4) enemy

Page 22
Practice session:
1) a) iii b) i
2) Answers could include: old, nuts,
wizard, leader
3) They didn't know who the children
were or why they were there; they
might turn out like the Malvos.
4) 1, 4, 3, 2
5) Answers should mention that Milo is
clever, interested in Sparkopolis and
likes reading books.
6) The Malvos are bad characters.
Gwanwyn told the children never to
trust a Malvo. Remember the mistake
we made with the Malvos! The
children… were warned to stay clear of
the Malvos…
7) Answers will vary.

Page 23
Milo's challenge:
Answers will vary.

How to use the CD-ROM

The CD-ROM is designed to provide your child with lots of exciting activities to help them to develop and practise core skills in English. You can also find a range of additional resources that you can print out and complete with your child. These are in the parents' section.

The Main Menu Screen

Parents
If you are a parent, click on the PARENTS button on the left hand side. You can also find a whole load of extra things from activity sheets to pictures of your guides.

Children
If you are a child go straight to the CHILDREN button and find the activities on the colourful map.

Help
If you need help or further information about Spark Island, click on the HELP button.

Scores
To find out how you can score and save points, called megahops, click on the SCORES button.

Your guides to Spark Island

Have fun!!

The Spark Gang are your guides. They will help you to explore the CD-ROM and get the most out of Spark Island.

Installation instructions
This CD-ROM requires a Windows 95 (or above) PC or a Power Macintosh, with Internet Explorer or a similar browser installed. It does not require you to have any internet access. Your screen should be set to display in thousands of colours and at a resolution of 800 x 600 pixels or higher.

Technical Specifications
These CD-ROMs are designed to work on any reasonably modern computer, which will have at least the technical specifications given below.

PC
Microsoft Windows 95/NT 4.0 or higher with a web browser installed
Pentium-class processor 133Mhz or above with 32MB RAM
SVGA compatible graphics, 4x speed CD-ROM drive and a sound card
On a PC the CD-ROM should install automatically. Once installed, go to the Start menu, then click Programs and click on the Spark Island icon in the Programs menu. Once the Spark Island icon has been installed, the CD-ROM should run automatically the next time it is inserted into the CD-ROM drive. If it does not, please select "Run" from the Start menu and type d:\spark.exe, where d:\ is the letter designated to your CD-ROM drive.
Note that the program will not run without the CD-ROM in your CD drive.

Macintosh
System 8.x or above
PowerPC processor, 333 Mhz or greater
64MB memory
The Spark Island icon will appear on your desktop when the CD-ROM is inserted. Open the CD-ROM by double-clicking on its icon, then double-click on the Spark Island icon. If it does not, please open the CD-ROM once it is displayed on your desktop and double-click on the Spark Island icon.
Note that the program will not run without the CD-ROM in your CD drive.

Discover secret treasure on Spark Island!

Come and explore at www.sparkisland.com/world4
– there are some free goodies waiting for you!

Spark Learning Limited, 28 Bruton Street, London W1J 6QW
Website: www.sparkisland.com

Published by BBC Educational Publishing, BBC Worldwide, 80 Wood Lane, London W12 0TT

Every effort has been made to trace copyright holders and obtain their permission for the use of copyright material.
The authors and publishers will gladly receive information enabling them to rectify any error or omission in subsequent editions.

All facts are correct at time of going to press.

Published 2002
Text © Spark Island

British Library Cataloguing in Publication Data
A CIP record for this book is available from the British Library.

ISBN: 0 563 54651 4

Printed in Singapore.